From Rote to Note

12 PIANO STUDIES

Late Elementary to Early Intermediate Piano Studies That Reinforce Theory and Technique
Designed to Be Taught without Traditional Notation

E. L. Lancaster *and* Omar Roy

Contents

© 2023 by the Frances Clark Center

Piano Education Press

The Frances Clark Center

90 Main Street, P.O. Box 651

Kingston, NJ 08528

ISBN-13: 978-1-7377237-4-5

About This Book

From Rote to Note, Book 2 contains twelve studies that reinforce keyboard theory and technique. Each study is based on a theoretical or technical concept that students encounter at late elementary to early intermediate levels of study and is designed to be taught from a musical map without the aid of traditional notation. Once students can play from the abstract representation, they can examine the notated score. They move intellectually from rote to note, experiencing musical elements before relating them to notation.

This book is geared toward students of varying age groups and can easily be adapted into existing curriculums. It is especially useful for students who play other instruments and are familiar with rhythm notation. Students who are not familiar with rhythm notation can learn the rhythms by ear after hearing teacher demonstrations.

Each study includes the following:

- An abstract that maps the piece to aid with memory and practice at home

- Traditional notation of the piece

- A teacher section that identifies the piece's concept, gives steps for introducing the musical map, and outlines strategies for teaching the study by rote

About Rote Teaching

Rote teaching can be defined as a student imitating a teacher or a recording of music with minimal reference to a musical score. It has several benefits for students and can even aid in securing note-reading skills if integrated into a solid curriculum that combines rote- and note-based learning. It forms the basis of developing literate, independent musicians. Some advantages of rote teaching follow:

Artistry: Students can apply listening skills to focus on artistically bringing out musical character.

Creative Exploration: Students can improvise on the rote materials, using their own musical ideas to further explore the concept.

Ear Training: Students learn to listen more intently to identify concepts.

Memory: Students begin to memorize the music from the first introduction to the pieces.

Motivation: Students are motivated by rote instruction since they can often play more difficult music than they can read.

Musical Understanding: Students can explore theoretical concepts such as phrase structure and form.

Pattern Recognition: Students learn to identify patterns visually from the abstract representation and aurally from hearing the music.

Sound to Symbol: Students can fully experience musical ideas before encountering the symbols for these concepts.

Technical Development: Students can focus on the technical aspects of playing without having to be concerned with reading notation.

Allegretto in C Major

In each measure, the hands alternate playing legato parallel thirds on white keys.

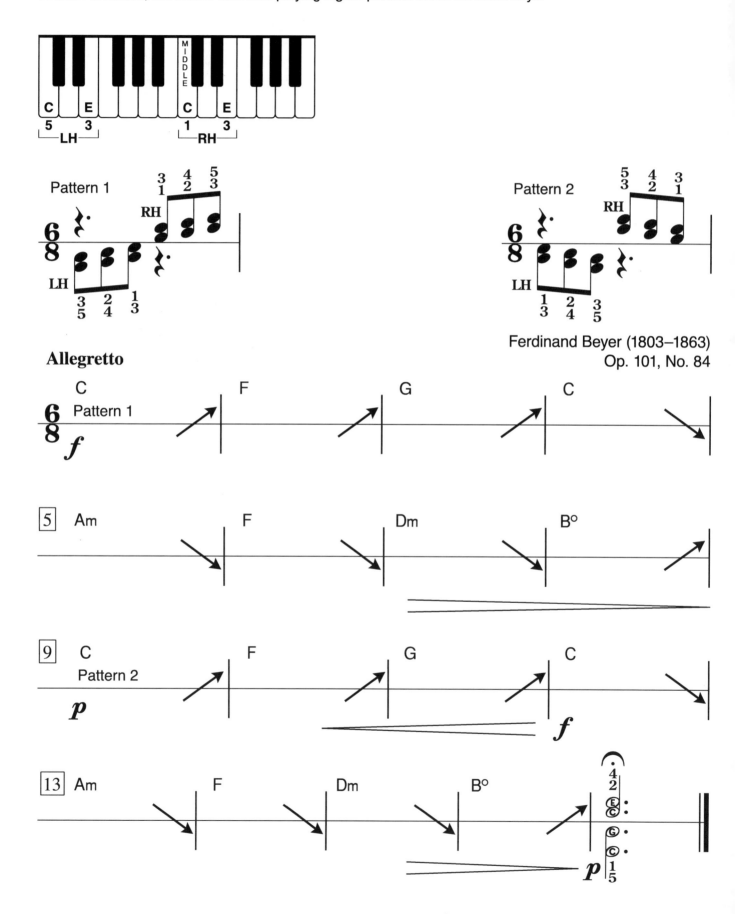

Ferdinand Beyer (1803–1863)
Op. 101, No. 84

Allegretto in C Major

Ferdinand Beyer (1803–1863)
Op. 101, No. 84

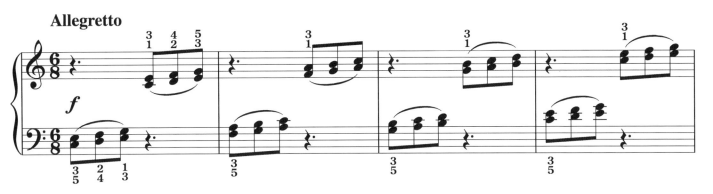

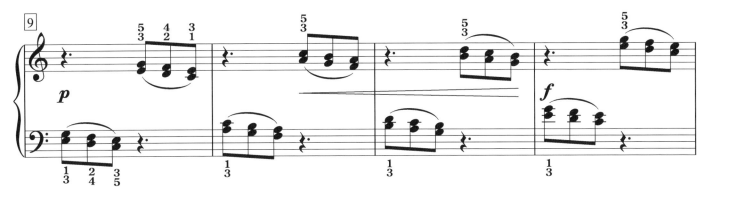

6

TEACHER

Allegretto in C Major (Thirds)

Introduce and Explain Map

1. Pitches above the horizontal line are played with the RH; pitches below the line are played with the LH.

2. Each of the two patterns plays thirds on white keys within a five-finger pattern. Pattern 1 with ascending thirds is played in mm. 1–8. Pattern 2 with descending thirds is played in mm. 9–16.

3. Chord symbols indicate the five-finger patterns to be used throughout the piece, while arrows indicate the direction to move to the next pattern.

4. Letter names and finger numbers are given for the final measure of the piece.

Demonstrate and Teach by Rote

1. Demonstrate the two patterns at the top of the map.

2. Block the chord hands together for each new pattern.

3. Block the chord hands separately (LH followed by the RH) for each new pattern. While one hand is playing the chord, the other hand moves to the location of the next chord during the rest.

4. Play the LH of mm. 1–8 as written; then, play the RH. Then, play alternating hands.

5. Play the LH of mm. 9–16 as written; then, play the RH. Then, play alternating hands.

6. Play m. 16 using pattern 2, concluding the with final chord in m. 17.

7. Play the entire piece, using pattern 1 for mm. 1–8 and pattern 2 for mm. 9–16.

Moderato in C Major

In this piece, the RH plays parallel sixths with fingers 1 and 5. Play the RH nonlegato.

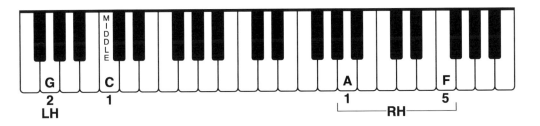

Cornelius Gurlitt (1820–1901)
Op. 82, No. 62

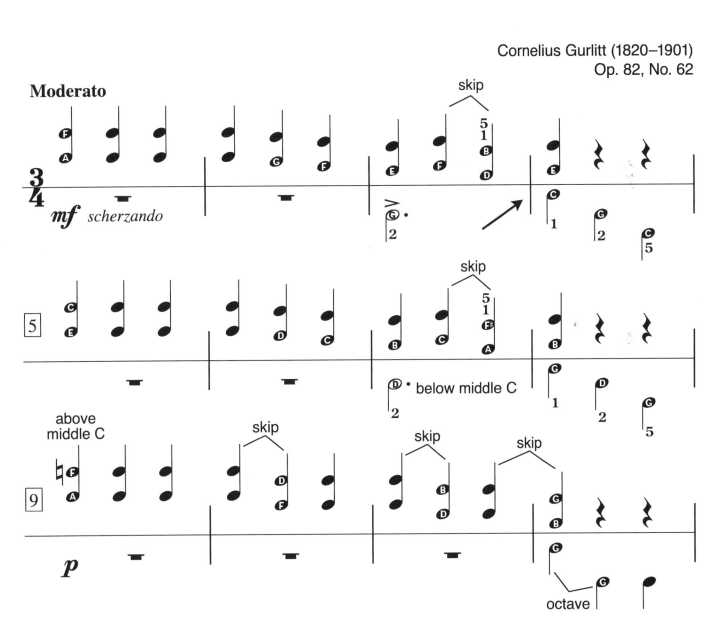

13–16 | Repeat mm. 9–12.

17–20 | Repeat mm. 5–8, but *f*.

21–24 | Repeat mm. 1–4 with RH an octave lower, but *f*.

Moderato in C Major

Cornelius Gurlitt (1820–1901)
Op. 82, No. 62

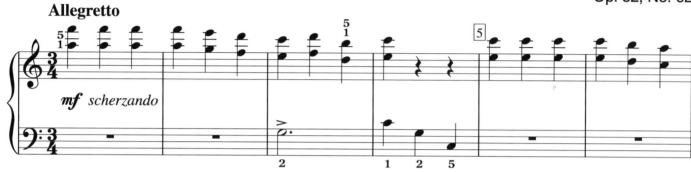

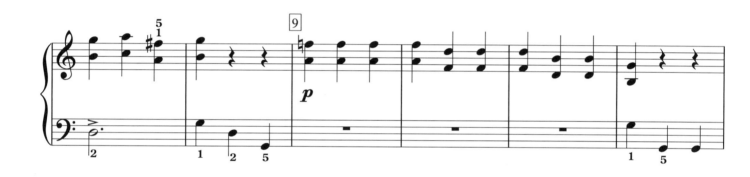

Moderato in C Major (Sixths)

Introduce and Explain Map

1. Pitches above the horizontal line are played with the RH; pitches below the line are played with the LH.

2. Sixths in the RH are established in the first measure and continue throughout the entire piece.

3. Most sixths are repeated or move stepwise. If they are repeated (mm. 1–2, 5–6, 9–11), no letter names are given. When they move by step, the letter name for the bottom note is shown. When they skip, the skip is labeled, and letter names are shown for both notes following the skip.

4. Other letter names and finger numbers are given for the LH.

5. Notation is only shown for the first three lines. The last three lines are repeats of measures from the first three lines with different dynamics in mm. 17–24.

Demonstrate and Teach by Rote

1. Demonstrate consistent fingering of sixths in mm. 1–2, emphasizing that students should concentrate on the thumb. Repeat this process for mm. 5–6 and mm. 9–10.

2. Find the LH pitches for the cadences in mm. 3–4, 7–8, and 12.

3. Practice the cadences in mm. 3–4, 7–8, and 11–12. First, play hands separately. Then, play hands together.

4. Discuss how mm. 5–8 are repeated for mm. 17–20 (but in a different order).

5. Discuss how mm. 1–4 are repeated an octave lower for mm. 21–24.

6. Play the entire piece, observing the rests throughout.

Étude in D Major

In each measure, the LH and RH alternate playing ascending broken chords and inversions while playing legato. Smoothly connect the chords from hand to hand.

Use the damper pedal, changing at the beginning of each measure.

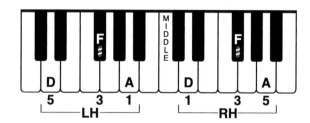

Cornelius Gurlitt (1820–1901)
Op. 82, No. 47

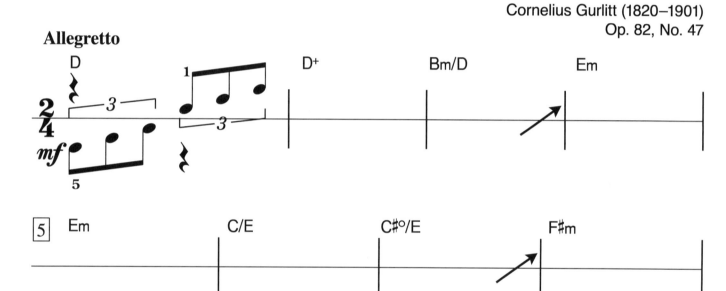

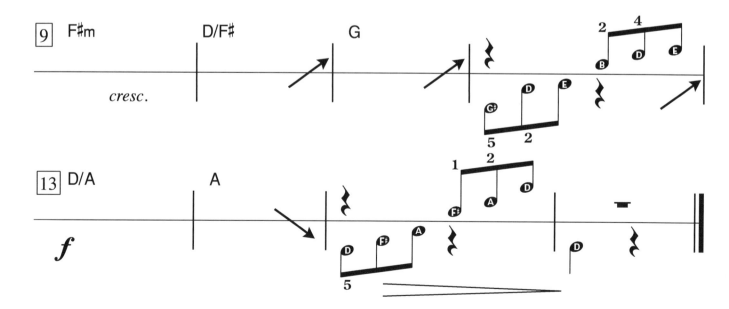

Étude in D Major

Cornelius Gurlitt (1820–1901)
Op. 82, No. 47

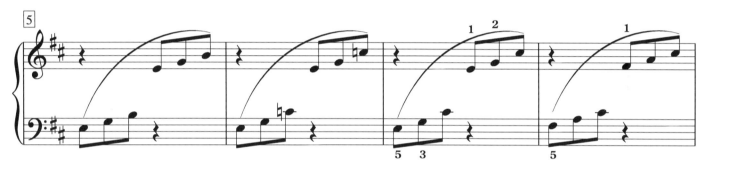

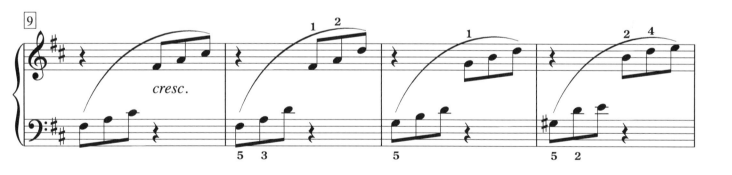

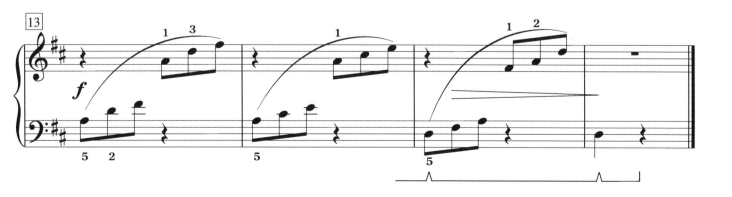

Étude in D Major (Ascending Broken Chords and Inversions)

Introduce and Explain Map

1. Pitches above the horizontal line are played with the RH; pitches below the line are played with the LH.

2. Chords and inversions are indicated above the RH unless each hand plays a different inversion. In mm. 12, 15, and 16 (where each hand plays a different inversion), letter names and finger numbers are given for individual pitches. Use standard fingering for root position chords and inversions.

3. When a change of position is necessary, arrows indicate the direction to move to the next chord.

Demonstrate and Teach by Rote

Work in groups of four measures.

1. Block each LH chord; then, block each RH chord.

2. Block the chords, alternating hands.

3. Play as broken chords, alternating hands.

4. Use the damper pedal, changing at the beginning of each measure.

Étude in A Minor

In each measure, the RH and LH alternate playing descending broken chords and inversions while playing legato. Smoothly connect the chords from hand to hand.

Use the damper pedal, changing at the beginning of each measure.

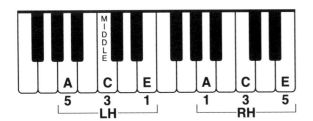

Ludvig Schytte (1848–1909)
Op. 160, No. 16

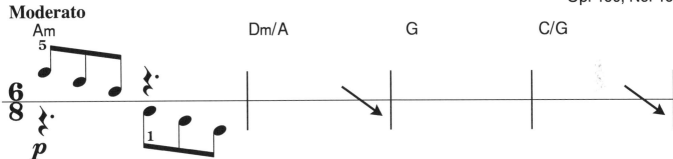

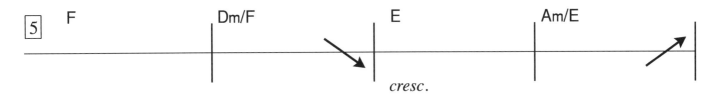

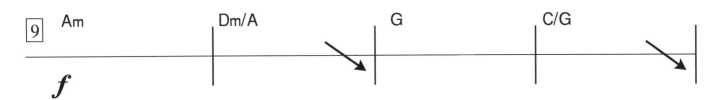

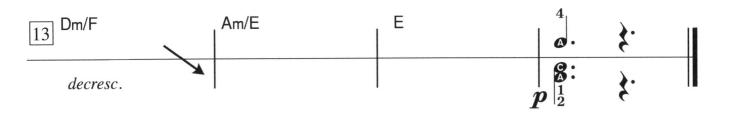

Étude in A Minor

Ludwig Schytte (1848–1909)
Op. 160, No. 16

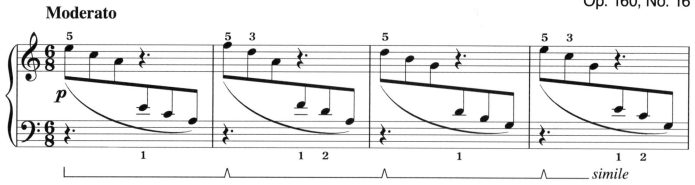

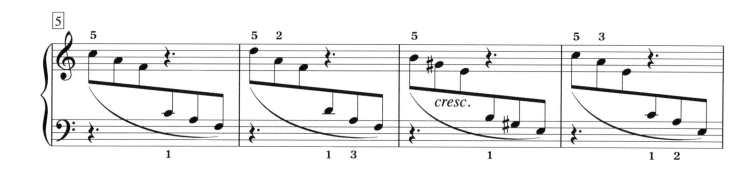

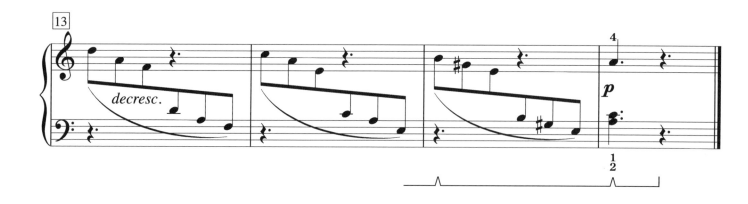

TEACHER

Étude in A Minor (Descending Broken Chords and Inversions)

Introduce and Explain Map

1. Pitches above the horizontal line are played with the RH; pitches below the line are played with the LH.

2. Chords and inversions are indicated above the RH. Use standard fingering for root position chords and inversions. In m. 16, letter names and finger numbers are given for individual pitches.

3. Arrows indicate the direction to move toward the next chord.

Demonstrate and Teach by Rote

Work in groups of four measures.

1. Block each RH chord; then, block each LH chord.

2. Block the chords, alternating hands.

3. Play as broken chords, alternating hands.

4. Use damper pedal, changing at the beginning of each measure.

Étude in C Major

In each measure, the hands alternate playing five-finger patterns in different positions. Play legato, except where staccatos are marked.

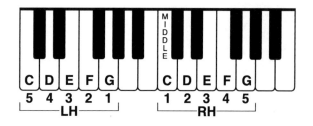

Louis Köhler (1820–1886)
Op 157, No. 1

Moderato

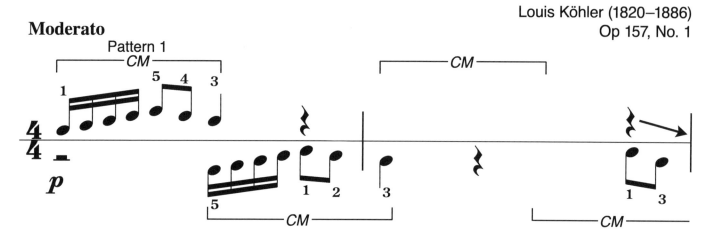

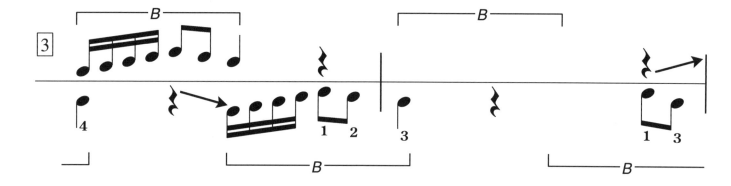

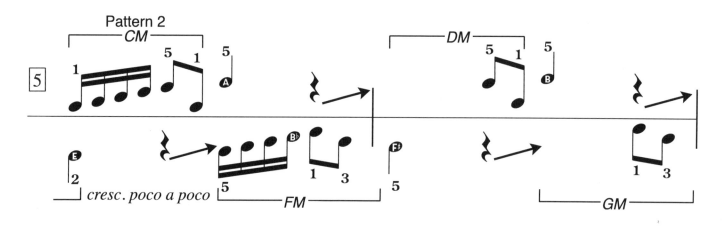

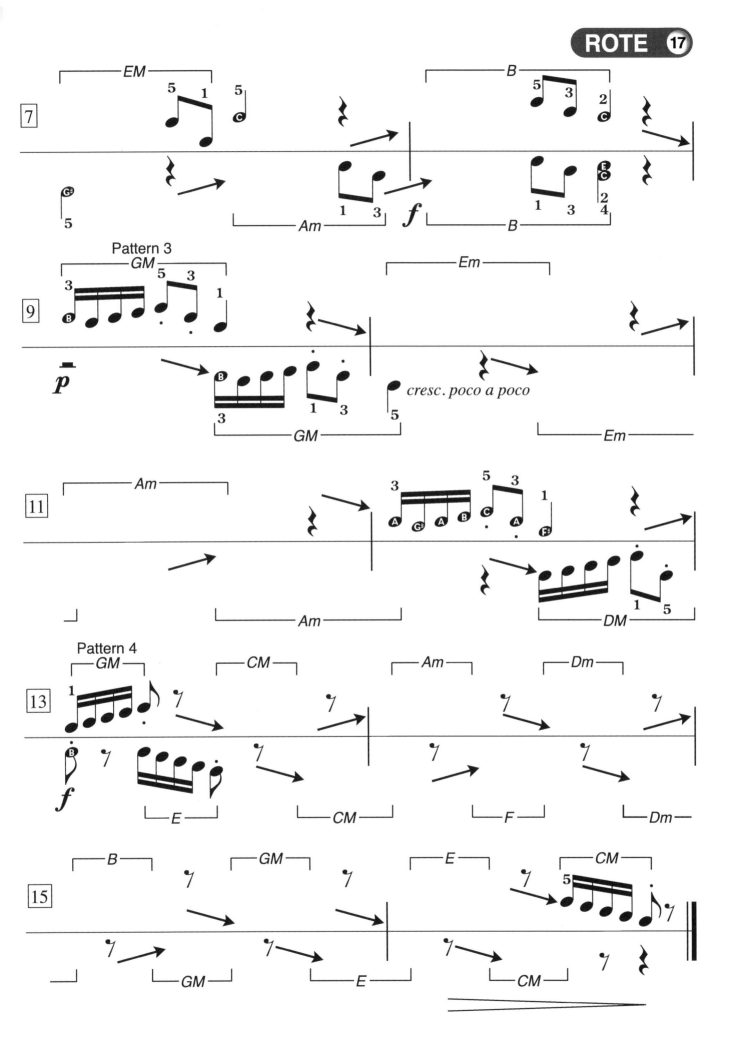

Étude in C Major

Louis Köhler (1820–1886)
Op 157, No. 1

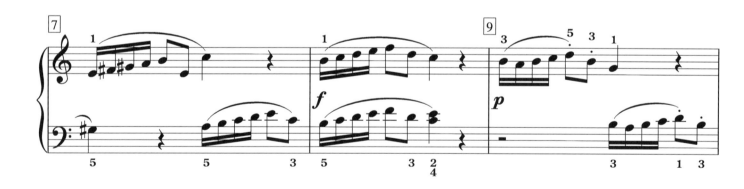

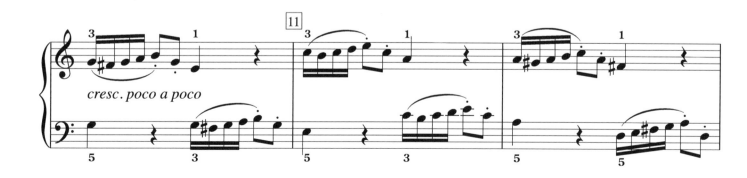

TEACHER

Étude in C Major (Five-Finger Patterns)

Introduce and Explain Map

1. Pitches above the horizontal line are played with the RH; pitches below the line are played with the LH.

2. The lettered labels represent five-finger patterns (not chord symbols). Letters without an M (major) or m (minor) are to be played with only white keys (mm. 3–4, 8, 13–16).

3. Arrows indicate the direction to move to the next pattern.

4. The piece consists of four different types of five-finger patterns. After a pattern is introduced, labels that follow indicate that the rhythm pattern is repeated and the pitch pattern is transposed.

5. Letter names and accidentals are given for individual notes and unique patterns where necessary (mm. 5–8, 12–13).

Demonstrate and Teach by Rote

1. Demonstrate and play pattern 1 in the RH (mm. 1–4). Then, play the patterns in the LH (mm. 1–4).

2. Demonstrate and play pattern 2 in the RH (mm. 5–8). Then, play the patterns in the LH (mm. 5–8).

3. Demonstrate and play pattern 3 in the RH (mm. 9–12). Then, play the patterns in the LH (mm. 9–12).

4. Demonstrate and play pattern 4 in the RH (mm. 13–16). Then, play the patterns in the LH (mm. 13–16).

5. Following the arrows to move in the appropriate direction, block the five-finger patterns for each hand separately. Then, block the patterns alternating hands as written (except for m. 8 where patterns should be blocked hands together).

6. Play the entire piece as written.

Allegretto in A Minor

This piece features A natural minor and C major scales in a musical context.
Use standard fingering for these scales while playing legato throughout.

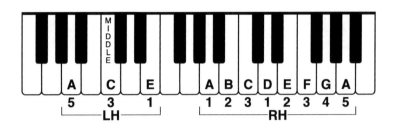

Allegretto

Cornelius Gurlitt (1820–1901)
Op. 82, No. 52

Allegretto in A Minor

Cornelius Gurlitt (1820–1901)
Op. 82, No. 52

TEACHER

Allegretto in A Minor (RH Scale Fingering)

Introduce and Explain Map

1. Pitches above the horizontal line are played with the RH; pitches below the line are played with the LH.

2. The scale pattern in m. 1 is played in mm. 5 and 13. The same pattern is played in C major in m. 9.

3. Starting pitches and finger numbers are given when the RH shifts positions (mm. 3, 7–8, 11, 15–16).

4. Letter names and finger numbers are given for some notes and chords.

5. Arrows indicate the direction to move for the next pattern or notes.

Demonstrate and Teach by Rote

1. Review the fingering for the opening octave and descending scales in mm. 1 and 9.

2. Find the starting note for each different RH position in mm. 3, 7–8, 11, and 15–16.

3. Play the RH for the entire piece.

4. Find the intervals and chords for the LH. Then, play the LH for the entire piece.

5. Block the notes in both hands when they play together in mm. 1, 3–4, 7–8, 11–12, and 15–16.

6. Play the entire piece, paying attention to rests.

Étude in C Major

In this piece, the hands alternate playing white-key scales starting on different pitches. Play legato throughout, paying attention to accents.

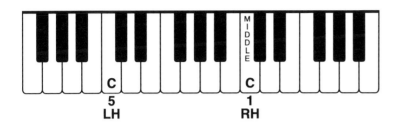

Moderato

Louis Köhler (1820–1886)
Op. 157, No. 4

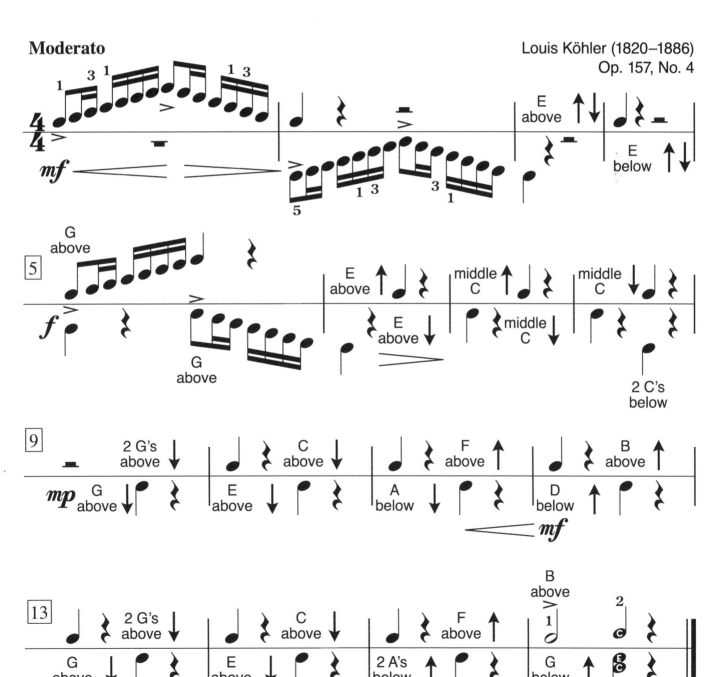

Étude in C Major

Louis Köhler (1820–1886)
Op 157, No. 4

TEACHER

Étude in C Major (Scale Fingering)

Introduce and Explain Map

1. Pitches above the horizontal line are played with the RH; pitches below the line are played with the LH.

2. The starting pitch is given for each white-key scale in its relationship to middle C. The word *above* means above middle C; the word *below* means below middle C. All scales use standard fingering for the C major scale. Arrows indicate the direction the scale moves— up, down, or up and down.

3. The basic rhythm patterns are introduced in mm. 1–2 and 5. The ascending and descending pattern in mm. 1–2 is used in mm. 3–4. Either an ascending or descending pattern (determined by arrows) is used in mm. 5–16.

4. Letter names are given for other notes where needed (mm. 8, 16).

Demonstrate and Teach by Rote

1. Demonstrate the ascending and descending fingering for the C major scale in both hands.

2. Find the starting pitches for each RH scale. Then, find the starting pitches for each LH scale.

3. Play the RH scales in mm. 1–4. Then, play the LH scales in mm. 2–5.

4. Play the RH for the entire piece. Then, play the LH.

5. Play the entire piece with both hands, adding accents to the first note of each scale pattern.

Prelude in B-flat Major

Use the damper pedal for the first two beats of m. 1 and for each chord in mm. 6–7 and 10–11.

Giuseppe Concone (1801–1861)
Op. 37, No. 5

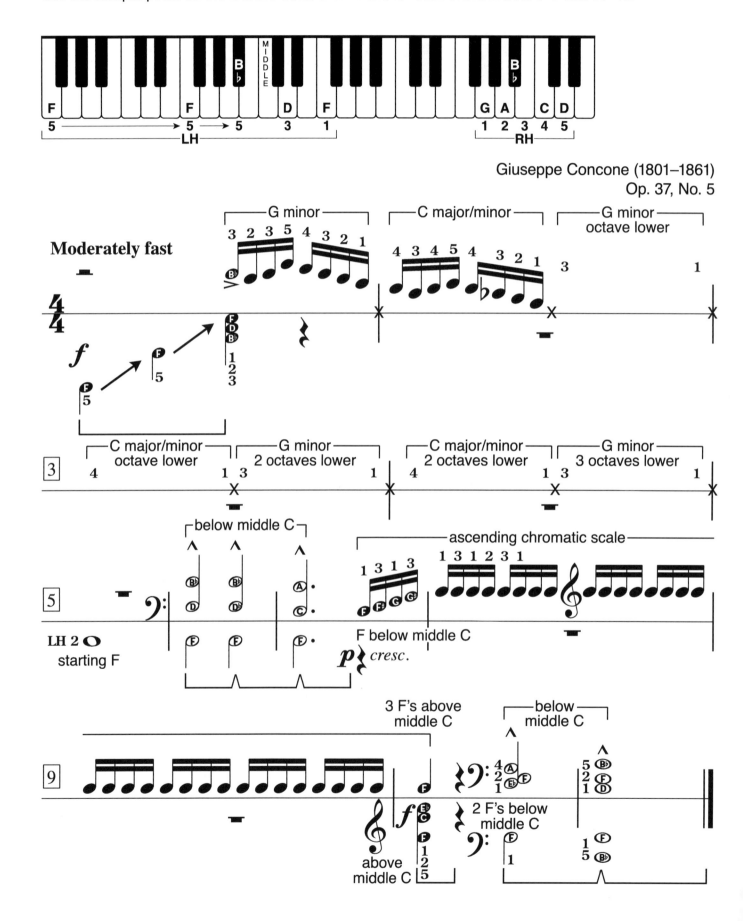

Prelude in B-flat Major

Giuseppe Concone (1801–1861)
Op. 37, No. 5

Moderately fast

TEACHER

Prelude in B-flat Major (Chromatic Scale)

Introduce and Explain Map

1. Pitches above the horizontal line are played with the RH; pitches below the line are played with the LH.

2. In both hands, letter names are shown for individual notes, intervals, and chords.

3. In mm. 1–4, the RH plays a descending melody of alternating five-finger patterns connected by crossovers (at each *X*).

4. In mm. 7–10, the RH plays an ascending chromatic scale.

5. Keyboard locations are indicated by the beginning starting position, their relationship to middle C, and markings that indicate to play an octave, two octaves, or three octaves lower.

Demonstrate and Teach by Rote

1. Demonstrate the RH pattern in the second half of m. 1 and the first half of m. 2. Then, play that pattern an octave lower, two octaves lower, and three octaves lower. Connect the pattern in the different octaves to play the RH of mm. 1–4.

2. Locate the starting position for the chromatic scale in the RH starting on beat 4 of m. 7. Use traditional scale fingering to play the chromatic scale for three octaves ending on the second F above middle C.

3. Find the individual notes, intervals, and chords in the LH of mm. 1 and 5. Then, find them in mm. 6–7 and 10–11 where the hands play together.

4. Play the entire piece, adding the indicated damper pedal in mm. 1, 6–7, and 10–11.

Prelude in G Minor

Use the damper pedal for the chords in mm. 8–9.

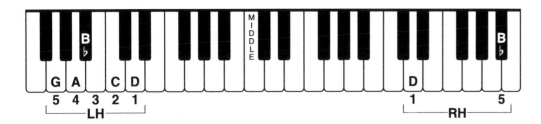

Giuseppe Concone (1801–1861)
Op. 37, No. 6

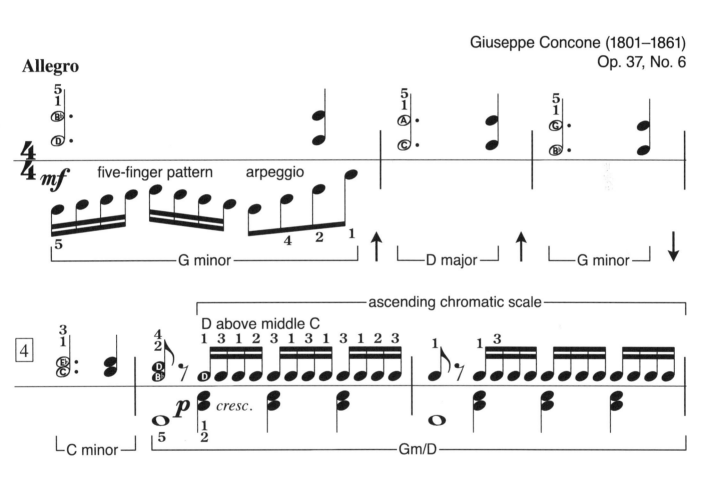

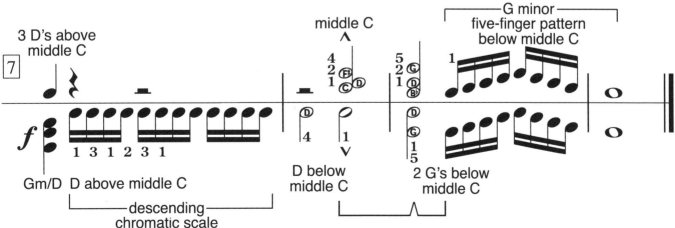

Prelude in G Minor

Giuseppe Concone (1801–1861)
Op. 37, No. 6

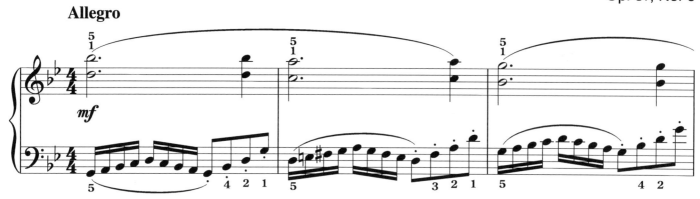

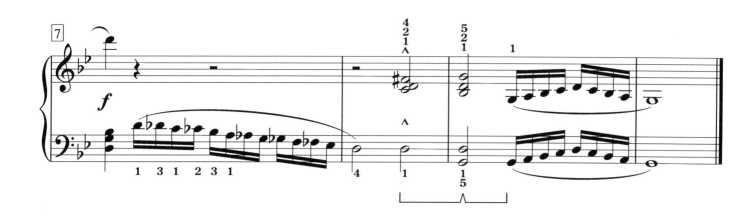

TEACHER

Prelude in G Minor (Chromatic Scale)

Introduce and Explain Map

1. Pitches above the horizontal line are played with the RH; pitches below the line are played with the LH.

2. In both hands, letter names are shown for individual notes, intervals, and chords.

3. The RH plays
   - sixths and thirds (mm. 1–5)
   - an ascending chromatic scale (mm. 5–7)
   - chords followed by a five-finger pattern (mm. 8–10)

4. The LH plays
   - a five-finger pattern and arpeggio (mm. 1–4)
   - an inverted chord over a held bass (mm. 5–6)
   - a chord followed by a descending chromatic scale (m. 7)
   - single notes, a fifth, and a five-finger pattern (mm. 8–10)

5. Arrows in mm. 1–3 indicate the direction to move for the next pattern.

Demonstrate and Teach by Rote

1. Demonstrate the LH pattern in m. 1, and play the same pattern in the keys shown in mm. 2–4.

2. In the LH of mm. 5–7, find the G minor chord in second inversion. Play the bottom note of the chord on beat 1 of mm. 5–6 and the top two notes of the chord on the remaining beats, ending with a complete chord on beat 1 of m. 7.

3. Play the LH descending chromatic scale in mm. 7–8 for one octave using traditional scale fingering.

4. Demonstrate the single notes, interval, and G minor five-finger pattern in the LH of mm. 8–10.

5. Find the intervals in the RH of mm. 1–5.

6. Play the RH ascending chromatic scale in mm. 5–6 for one octave using traditional scale fingering. Play again an octave higher in mm. 6–7.

7. Demonstrate the chords and G minor five-finger pattern in the RH of mm. 8–10.

8. Play the entire piece, adding damper pedal to connect the chords in mm. 8–10.

Prelude in A Minor

Giuseppe Concone (1801–1861)
Op. 37, No. 2

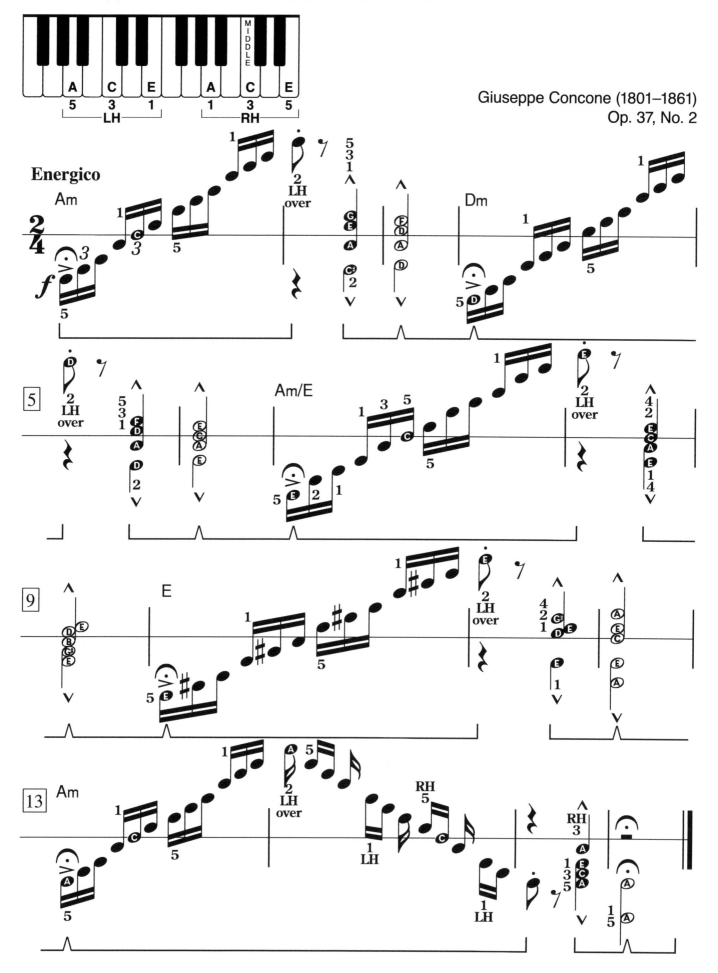

Prelude in A Minor

Giuseppe Concone (1801–1861)
Op. 37, No. 2

TEACHER

Prelude in A Minor (Hand-over-Hand Broken Chords)

Introduce and Explain Map

1. The horizontal line represents middle C. Notes with stems going up are for the RH; notes with stems going down are for the LH.

2. The chord symbols represent the hand-over-hand broken chords (mm. 1, 4, 7, 10, 13–15).

3. At the top of each hand-over-hand pattern, the LH plays a single staccato note (mm. 2, 5, 8, 11, 14).

4. Letter names are given for individual notes and chords throughout.

Demonstrate and Teach by Rote

Help the student locate each starting position on the keyboard in steps 1–4 below:

1. Demonstrate the hand-over-hand broken chords and the LH crossover in mm. 1–2. Continue in a similar manner in mm. 4–5, 7–8, and 10–11.

2. Demonstrate the ascending and descending hand-over-hand broken chords in mm. 13–15.

3. Find the RH chords and intervals in mm. 2–3, 5–6, 8–9, and 11–12 and the single note in m. 15.

4. Find the LH notes, intervals, and chords in mm. 2–3, 5–6, 8–9, 11–12, and 15–16.

5. Play the notes, intervals, and chords hands together in mm. 2–3, 5–6, 8–9, 11–12, and 15.

6. Play the entire piece, adding pedal.

Étude in D Minor

Pedal each arpeggio and quarter-note chord.

Cornelius Gurlitt (1820–1901)
Op. 82, No. 67

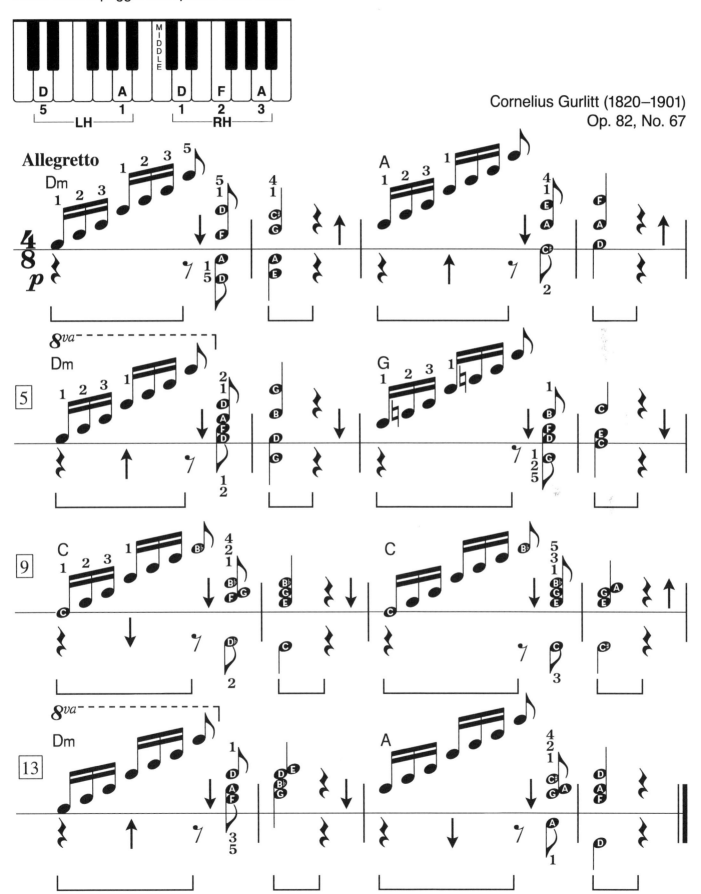

Étude in D Minor

Cornelius Gurlitt (1820–1901)
Op. 82, No. 67

TEACHER

Étude in D Minor (Arpeggios)

Introduce and Explain Map

1. The horizontal line represents middle C. Notes with stems going up are for the RH; notes with stems going down are for the LH.

2. Chord symbols identify the two-octave RH arpeggios. All arpeggios start on or above middle C.

3. Letter names are given for individual notes, intervals, and chords throughout.

4. Arrows indicate the direction to move to the next note.

Demonstrate and Teach by Rote

Help the student locate each starting position on the keyboard in steps 1–3 below:

1. Demonstrate the arpeggios in mm. 1 and 3. Then, play all arpeggios. Note the *8va* sign in mm. 5 and 13. Start on the second D above middle C.

2. Find the RH intervals and single notes throughout. Then, play the top note of each arpeggio and practice the move between that note and the next interval.

3. Find the LH intervals and single notes throughout. Use the middle C line to help.

4. Play the intervals and single notes hands together throughout.

5. Play the entire piece, using the pedal to create a full, rich sound in the arpeggios and quarter-note chords.

Challenge: Play the arpeggios with the LH using fingering 5 3 2 1 3 2 1. Begin two octaves lower.

Prelude in F Major

No. 10 from *12 Little Pieces and Preludes*

Use the damper pedal, changing each measure. Play each LH quarter note *coll' 8va* (with an added octave below) in mm. 1–9, 11, and 13.

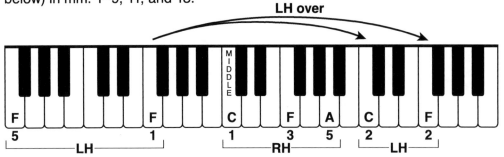

Henri Bertini (1798–1876)

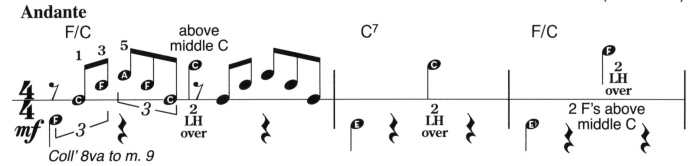

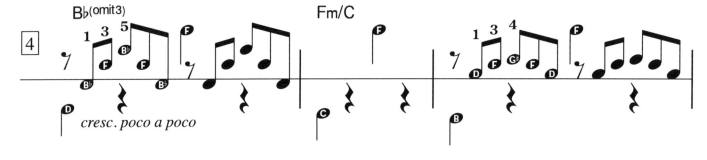

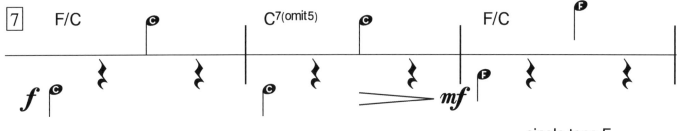

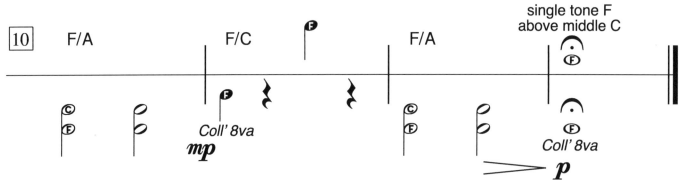

Prelude in F Major

No. 10 from *12 Little Pieces and Preludes*

Henri Bertini (1798–1876)

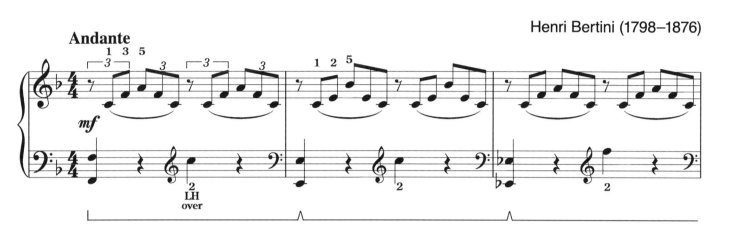

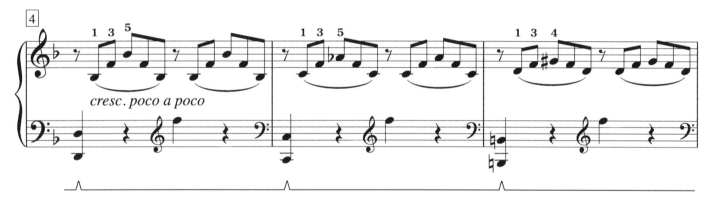

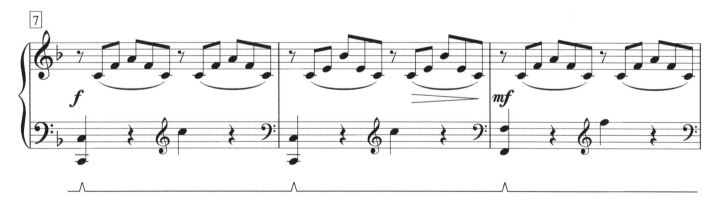

TEACHER

Prelude in F Major (Broken Chords and Hand-over-Hand Crossovers)

Introduce and Explain Map

1. The horizontal line represents middle C. Notes with stems going up are for the RH; notes with stems going down are for the LH.

2. The chord symbols represent the RH broken chords. All measures (except the last one) use the rhythm shown in m. 1. Exact notes for the chords in mm. 4 and 6 are shown. The RH plays a single note F above middle C in m. 13.

3. The LH quarter notes on beat 1 of each measure are the top notes of octaves below middle C (except for intervals of a fifth in mm. 10 and 12). The top note of the octave in m. 6 is two B's below middle C, and the top note of the octave in m. 13 is two F's below middle C.

4. Except for mm. 10, 12, and 13, the LH crosses over to play the C above middle C or the second F above middle C with finger 2 after each broken chord.

Demonstrate and Teach by Rote

1. Find and block the RH chords in each measure.

2. Find each octave or interval of a fifth in the LH, and then move up to the C or F higher on the keyboard.

3. Play the LH and block the chords in the RH of each measure.

4. Play the entire piece as written, using the pedal to capture the changing harmonies in each measure.

Made in the USA
Middletown, DE
28 February 2023

25875768R00024